MEET ALL THESE FRIENDS IN BUZZ BOOKS:

Thomas the Tank Engine
Fireman Sam
The Animals of Farthing Wood
Skeleton Warriors
Puppy In My Pocket
Kitty In My Pocket
Pony In My Pocket

First published in Great Britain in 1996 by Buzz Books
an imprint of Reed Children's Books
Michelin House, 81 Fulham Road, London SW3 6RB
and Auckland, Melbourne, Singapore and Toronto.

Based on a Martin Gates Production
Copyright ©1996 BMG Entertainment
Licensed by Just Licensing Ltd
Text copyright © 1996 Reed International Books Limited
Illustrations by Arkadia copyright © 1996 Reed International Books Limited

ISBN 1 85591 555 3

Printed in Italy

Toad of Toad Hall

Story by Katie Vandyck
from the animated series

Toad had just returned from the biggest adventure of his life. He had escaped from prison disguised as a washerwoman and only narrowly avoided recapture while hitching a lift on a train. He had tussled with a barge woman, stolen her horse and sold it to a gypsy. Finally, he had hijacked the very same

car he had stolen, crashed it and only just
managed to escape by diving into the river.
At last he had been washed up at Rat's
river bank home to a surprisingly cool
reception. Rat had grave news to relate.
Toad Hall had been taken over by the
Wild Wooders.

Rat explained that while Toad was in
prison, Badger and Mole had stayed in Toad
Hall to keep it safe. One night, however,
hundreds of weasels, stoats and ferrets had
broken in. Badger and Mole had done what
they could to fight them off but were hugely
outnumbered. They had been beaten with
sticks and turned out into the cold. Since
then the Wild Wooders had been living in
Toad Hall, eating Toad's food and telling
everyone they were there for good. Toad was
furious. Before Rat could stop him he seized
a stick and headed off to Toad Hall.

Toad stormed up the road muttering
angrily to himself. As he neared the front
gate, suddenly up popped a ferret with
a gun.

"Who comes here?" hissed the ferret.

"Stuff and nonsense," cried the angry
Toad. "What do you mean by talking to me
like that? Come out of it at once or I'll . . ."

But before Toad could finish his sentence the ferret had taken aim and fired. Toad flung himself to the ground as the bullet whistled past his head. He scrambled to his feet and scampered down the road as fast as he could.

Toad would not give up. He rowed Rat's boat up river to Toad Hall. Two ferrets were lying in wait for him on a bridge. As he approached them, the ferrets sent a stone crashing through the bottom of the boat, sinking it and flinging Toad into the river. Rat was very angry when he heard what Toad had done. He convinced Toad not to attempt any more madcap rescue operations until they had heard from Badger and Mole. The two loyal creatures had stayed out in every kind of weather, keeping an eye on Toad Hall and planning its recapture.

Toad declared that he would search out
his brave friends and share their hardships.
He would start at once . . . just as soon as he
had had his supper! Suddenly there was a
loud knock at the door. Toad shot behind an
armchair and sat there quivering with fright,
but it was only Badger and Mole, unkempt
and bringing bad news. Mole explained that
Toad Hall had been extremely well fortified
by the invaders.

"There are sentries posted everywhere and when they see us – they laugh!"
He added, "It's useless to think of attacking the place, they're much too strong for us."

Toad was in despair.

"Cheer
up Toady!"
said Badger,
comfortingly.
"I'm going to
tell you a great secret."

Toad perked up immediately.

"There is an underground passage that
leads from the river bank, right up into the
butler's pantry at Toad Hall." Badger
continued. "Your father gave me permission
to tell you but only if you were ever in a
real fix."

Badger explained that the Wild Wooders were to hold a birthday banquet for the Chief Weasel in the dining hall, next to the butler's pantry. It was to be the following night. The four of them would creep quietly along the passageway, up into the pantry . . .

"With our pistols and swords . . ." added Rat.

"And rush in upon them," finished Badger.

The next day, dressed in Toad's washerwoman disguise, Mole went up to the Stoat sentries and offered to do their laundry. When they rudely refused, Mole pretended to be angry.

"My daughter, who washes for Mr Badger, says they're sending a hundred bloodthirsty Badgers, six boat loads of Rats with cutlasses and the Toads known as 'Death or Glory Toads' to attack the house tonight. So there won't be much of you lot left to wash tomorrow."

Toad was aghast at what Mole had done.
Badger, however, was impressed. He knew
that the Wild Wooders would now be very
frightened indeed.

By that evening Rat had armed himself and his friends and they set off into the night. Badger found the hole in the river bank that led to the secret passageway and scrambled in. Rat and Mole followed silently but Toad slipped and toppled into the water with a loud "splash!" Badger was very cross. "Make a fool of yourself again Toad and you'll certainly be left behind."

Toad did his best to behave but soon fell behind. Frightened at being left alone, he ran to catch up, bumped into Rat and sent them all flying.

They picked themselves up, Rat took a firm hold on Toad's shoulder and they marched on towards Toad Hall.

At last they reached the butler's pantry.
As they stood by the door they could hear
sounds of wild merriment coming from the
party. The Chief Weasel was entertaining
his followers with a most uncomplimentary
song about Toad. As he listened to their
laughter, Toad grew more and more angry.

"Just let me get at him!" he muttered, grinding his teeth.

"Hold hard a minute," warned Badger.

He drew himself up to his full height and addressed his friends, "Get ready, all of you!"

He raised his cudgel and flung the door wide open. "The hour has come," he cried, "follow me!"

Rat, Mole, Toad and Badger burst into
the hall; Badger swinging his cudgel, Rat
waving his pistols and Mole brandishing his
stick, uttering a dreadful cry. Toad, frenzied
with excitement and injured pride, went
straight for the Chief Weasel. They were four
against hundreds but to the panic stricken

weasels the hall seemed full of wild animals.
Tables and chairs went flying as the ferrets
fled in terror, tumbling over each other and
getting stuck in doorways in their rush to
escape. Five minutes later the room was
empty. The four friends had triumphed.

The next day the animals agreed there should be a celebration in honour of their victory. Toad suggested a dozen ways he might entertain his guests with stories and songs of his great adventures.

"No songs and no speeches," said Rat, firmly. "They are all boasting with vanity and self-praise."

Toad was deeply wounded. A tear trickled down his cheek. He sighed and said, "Henceforth, I will be a very different Toad. You shall never have occasion to blush for me again."

Pressing a handkerchief to his face he limped from the room.

The party was in full swing as Toad's friends waited impatiently for his triumphant entrance. As he stepped quietly into the room, they gathered round him and cheered him to the rooftops. He waved their compliments aside with a modest shake of his head. When they congratulated him on his courage and cleverness he murmured,

"Not at all," and, "on the contrary," and,
"Badger's was the mastermind, I merely
served in the ranks."

Badger and Rat watched in astonishment
as Toad made his way round the room,
humbly greeting his guests. He was a
changed Toad indeed.